A Chocolate Moose

for Dinner

written and illustrated by
FRED GWYNNE

A TRUMPET CLUB SPECIAL EDITION

ISBN 0-590-99515-4

Copyright © 1976 by Fred Gwynne.
All rights reserved. Published by Scholastic Inc.,
555 Broadway, New York, NY 10012,
by arrangement with Simon & Schuster Books
for Young Readers, a division of Simon & Schuster, Inc.
TRUMPET and the TRUMPET logo are registered
trademarks of Scholastic Inc.

12 11 10 9 8 7   4 5 6 7 8 9/0

Printed in the U.S.A.

For Keiron, Gaynor, Madyn, Evan, and Furlaud

Mommy says she had a chocolate moose for dinner last night.

And after dinner

she toasted Daddy.

there's a gorilla war.

Daddy says
he has trees
for all his shoes.

**Daddy says
lions pray on**

other  animals.

Daddy says he hates

the arms race.

Daddy says there should

Mommy says her

favorite painter is Dolly.

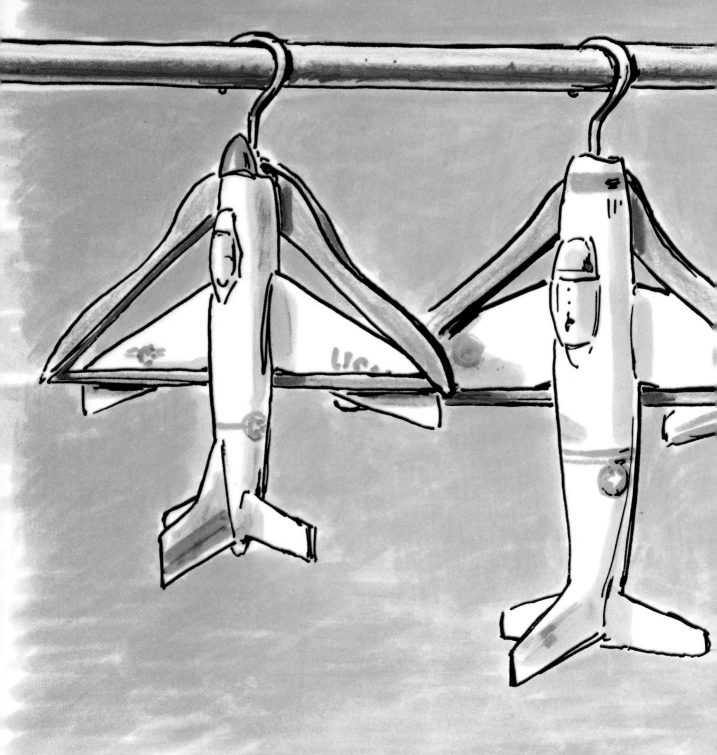

Mommy says there are airplane hangers.

**Daddy says
he has the best
fishing tackle.**

It says on TV
a man held up a bank.

He spent two years in the pen.

And he has just escaped and is now on the lamb.

watch out for the under toe.

**Daddy says he plays
the piano by ear.**

Daddy says that in college

people row in shells.

**And some row
in a single skull.**

Mommy says she's going to tell me about Santa Claws.

And Daddy says he's going to tell me the story of

the tortoise and the hair.

Stories like these drive me up a wall!